Evening Light

A Retrospect in Stories and Poems

by

Jemi Reis McDonald

MANDORLA BOOKS
WWW.MANDORLABOOKS.COM

For my husband and son with whom
being truly *known* was, and is, the
greatest honor and human gift.

TABLE OF CONTENTS

III.

Author's Note

These stories and poems span the years 1952 to 2022. Some include that entire period; some take place in a single hour. Yet as is true of any real life, they also telegraph one another, look back at each other and exist as independently acting individuals within the group.

Sometimes I see the whole range of my life and feel the intricacy of its considerable expanse; while other times I see a single simple truth outside of time.

I invite you to read each story or poem independently and be assisted by the dates I include as a general guide. Each piece has a singular truth that it wants to speak both for itself and together with the others.

Being among them now gathered, it is as though I am taking a late afternoon walk in the neighborhood after a long day. Each house I see along the way is beginning to be lit from within as those who live there settle in to their evenings. The lives behind each window are as familiar to me as if I too can hear, smell and move within the flow of being gratefully home at last.

Darkening blue light suffuses the sky and I share the humanness of being held within these warm rooms. I feel I am one of the family as I pass by even though we are all so very different now — each to each a mystery like the darkness rising from the shadows of the earth.

Offering us equally only the night ahead, to dream and hope.

I.

Where You All Are Now

In the night I reach for a light switch in a position I realize is from some previous house. The bare dark wall which meets my fingers is night-cool, a habitual place but no longer familiar. Standing there I wonder which room in what house I was reaching to illuminate. Is it the house we shared for twenty-six years in which everything changed in our lives except the location of the light switch?

All the switch could possibly reveal is the furniture we wore down day by day and the air there that would quietly surround our forms like transparent gloves as we entered then silently let us go as we exited.

The flow of those changes carries all the sounds in this room. The light switch might seem to be a kind of longed-for stasis-of-the-heart and the room it illuminated may contain all of the people I've loved in my life.

Perhaps they are still sleeping there, warm in the night then waking late on a Sunday morning. A room where I am known. A room where dawn light enters gently, gradually. A room where speech is unnecessary because all is said and will be said.

1987, April 4

We marry in a small, old theater on a hill in Claremont, California. He looks quite handsome in his tux even with the black eye from the mud-wrestling lady at the bachelor-party the night before. I ask him outright if he got laid, and he says no, and I believe him.

He smiles through all the wedding photos with the shiner and his matrimonial joy, leaning in and slightly down to stretch his long, gentle arms across my and my frail, dying aunt's shoulders. She is the angel of my life and now a member of his family. Our family. I am thirty-four, he is thirty-nine.

In the course of the wedding ceremony several hundred dollars in wedding-gift cash is stolen from the entryway table it never occurs to us to guard. During an earthquake six months later the rest of the gifts – fine oversized goblets from Neiman Marcus and one-of-a-kind ceramics from a gallery on Melrose – are hurled from the kitchen cabinets and shatter into drastic shards we later find all the way in the living room.

It's seven forty-two of a workday morning when the quake hits. We are drinking from our new fancy coffee cups and reading the LA Times when the first sharp, falling jolt hits and the violent shaking begins. I try to run out the front door through the living room. But my husband secures me shielded by his body in the doorjamb as I struggle against him saying, "No. No! I need to get out of here!"

We clean up the house and smashed wedding gifts. Three weeks later we win several thousand in the state lotto while drinking coffee at the same table, from lesser mugs.

• • •

By the time we are thirty-seven and forty-two, we have only an eleven percent chance of getting pregnant — everything is we, we, we, even though I will do the carrying. As we conceive the first time out with in vitro at a fertility clinic, I stare at the impersonal ceiling tiles above me and invoke a waking dream for luck — of a pelican gliding along a breaking wave. Its long slender wings poised just above the water's crest, searching, searching.

Later that night there is a dramatic storm and our bedroom is splashed with blue/white light that tensions the air with electricity. The walls tremble the thunder is so loud, its resonance tramping off into the far distance as though we have been abandoned in a giant's fit of pique. We laugh in fear and amazement, hold each other and settle in to the now gentling beat of the rain until finally we forget we are no longer awake.

Our son is born in May.

When he is nine months old, we leave the sky-slouching helicopters of LA and their invasive search-lights for the low-density, freeway-inaccessible town of Ojai an hour and a half away from my husband's work still in LA. Three months later the riots break out. When my husband gets home that afternoon he finds us up at the nearby school's athletic field where we go when our son gets restless. We guard him as he tries to walk, then as he rolls diagonally down the long grassy slope in slow motion. My husband commutes to LA for thirteen more years before he buys the business for himself and comes the rest of the way home.

From the black-eye onward we leave our mucked-up previous relationships behind and love each other all-out. My enduring sense of doom begins to wear away; his silent expectation to be cast aside turns out to be ill-founded.

• • •

We live happily to our twenty-fifth wedding anniversary and the next month he is diagnosed stage four, pancreatic. He is unapproachably, silently, furious for three continuous weeks. Then something in him shifts and everything is we, we, we — even though he will do the dying.

We get down to the hard work of not wasting time.

1952, The Blue

For the first few months of my life my father was also alive. But I only have visceral and scent memories of him, indelible as Japanese brush strokes that bleed cleanly into a thirsty weave of rice paper. He died at forty-six years in July of 1953 when I was seven months old.

Yet we made a pact, he and I, in a form that was not yet language. He relayed, in emotional ink, "I need to leave. You're going to be okay," and his knowing sank into my knowing straight from pupil-to-pupil blackness as he held me. It was a night black-ness but it was not frightening, it was merely another element of reality in the unseen field that holds all.

I knew he was with me and that time was without limit, without boundary and without fight or grasp.

His cheek was almost blue with dark stubble and he smelled of burning leaves and sweet scotch. The essential oil of his hair-scent was my own animal sig-nature. This was the same scent the man who later would become my husband would lean in close to smell, saying he could perceive its essence even un-der my perfume.

No pact would ever compare in life with that with my father and yet that pact would become a template for all essential pacts to come. In that way I would find you all by smell and even in the dark I could locate you all and have never lost any of you.

I listen to the silence of my father's words and answer with my own silence – ocean's yield listening; air's embrace surrounding; the letting go within being held. My father of night held the dimension of my world. May he live in my heart; may I love the gorgeous world for him.

As for the rest of my family, it seems that everyone was so busy with my father's dying, and all of the complications of his impending absence, practical and emotional, that I was put slightly aside. This was the first of many times in my life that "... an injustice was perpetrated in my favor," as my beloved aunt, my father's sister, defined it.

She said it that earliest time when I was given over to our neighbors Kaye and Benny to be watched as my father died; then she said it strategically on occasions in my later life if I was fired from a job or jilted by a restless lover.

But when I was an infant the favor lay in the specific place where I was put – high on a loping hill in far northern Malibu, California, near my father and mother's ranch. At the top of a steep, dirt driveway running through green chaparral and wild mustard which had just flowered a subtle bright yellow. At the end was Benny and Kaye's house, they being the local stone mason and his wife, the local babysitter.

That's where Kaye would hold me, woken crying from a nap, give me a bottle and watch my eyes emerge from woe to happy open wonderment. Later Kaye would tell me that I was "the smilingist child" she had ever met, good, and quiet, and when upset, soon over it. At the west side of their house was a huge bay window and under it, the nap bed. I spent most of the first days and two years of my life lying on the cream chenille covering this bed, corralled with pillows to prevent me from rolling onto the floorboards and the well-worn braided rug Kaye had made, herself pregnant, the first year of her marriage to Benny.

When I woke, Kaye would sit on that bed and feed me, then hoist me onto her chest and shoulder. It was the blue I would encounter there, beyond her warm anchoring and the window, down the hill, over the highway and far, far out to sea, that would never leave me. And if one could fathom my first and deepest heart, this sight would measure its sure core.

Over time as I gained sight focus and years, first I would see the hills and their sweep and descent, and then the light blue sky and its way of disappearing the more I sought to see it. Then my whole perception would be pulled to the deep, fathomless blue of the sea, itself surging and rolling into waves. Finally disappearing in a stunning and rare natural flat line where it joined back into the sky itself.

Hour after hour, I would never tire of watching it. And though every day, and even within the hours, suddenly, its whole mood and movement would shift, it was that blue itself, the way it tugged my whole self toward it, quieted, stunned with its never-endingness;

the way that color would lie under the storms and light-shift and re-colorings, lie and wait for me, peek through to me, that is the animal center of my being.

The Pacific itself, the massive wordless near-then-far trick of it, stirring and rolling, then flat, then, if I shifted my eyes just short of horizon, the hint of curvature, the place of departure from the sea, the caul of air, the form of earth and the empty containment of space itself.

They would say that I was a quiet one, but I was only busy drinking into my soul the many ways of the blue.

If Benny was there, the TV was always going and usually Kaye would go and sit with him and sew or knit. The soaps, the friendly jingle of commercials, the dramatic music, the My Little Margie theme, westerns.

Or the radio would be going by the couch and Benny would be cleaning his gun at the kitchen table. Sometimes my brothers Jake and Pip, who were three and four at that time, would be there, sad and quiet or fighting each other, being shushed because of me being there, too. Watching morosely as Benny explained the bolt, handle and the sight, holding it up while their eyes followed, chins in hands. Then explaining about rattlesnakes, where to look out for them, not to poke them. Benny's murmuring voice, occasionally animated with excitement.

This plain home with its uncomplicated people and its long quiet hours and its heart of sea and hills, will always be home to me, no matter how far I will go or how close I will come to where it used to be.

Its scent of coastal sage, and fine clay dust and the rot-and-cleanse of the plankton and breaking waves, was the greeting of my life. The man who left, my father, would, my whole life thereafter be carried to me on these scents and colors, would become utterly abstract and *at large* in the intelligence of the working of things, in the shifts of weather and the seasons, in the constancy that lay under the caprice of human relationships, like the deep blue of the sea – lying under the grey sky reflection or the whitecaps of the storms foretelling their arrivals; lying steadily under, always there.

This home, that smelled of Benny's gun oil, Kaye's famous white bread-and-butter lunch burgers and overall of Palmolive bar soap, would be my first perceived home. Unlike my parents' home that year, it was predictable and revolved slowly, hour after hour, around the rural rhythms of work, hunting, food preparation, baby maintenance and the bolts of cloth and yarn that Kaye would tend to when not cooking or feeding or clearing up after people or gently keeping her peace while being sassed by her own children, then teen-agers.

My first job, at two years old, was to scatter the pink rose petals at the large church wedding of Kaye's pale and luminescent blue-eyed oldest daughter. I got a few steps into it and froze. My mother jerked me by the arm out of the isle and whispered viciously, "How *could* you embarrass me like this? You brat!"

But then Kaye came, announcing her presence by bending over us, casting her soft shadow upon us. A shadow I reached for, and that reached for me.

"There now, she's just a baby honey," she said to my mother. "She's just spooked. You're going to be okay," and as she turned away, "Both of you." A flash of indignant hostility from my mother and then Kaye enveloped me and turned away with me in her arms.

She held me for the entire rest of the wedding until the cake cutting, after which I was lowered onto the brilliant green of the courtyard grass, my petticoats rising up like the flowers of a fallen vase. To then stand up and run on with the other toddlers, our fine tiny dress-up clothes becoming untucked or falling forgotten onto the grass, pale flags demarking the border of the country of children.

1958, Boy in the Room of Light

The boy who will become my husband is now eleven years old, with a white-blond buzz cut and he's a little chubby from over-enjoying his mother's Kentucky-coal-miner cooking. He is wearing a brown-and-white horizontally striped long-sleeve cotton t-shirt, as were popular in the 1950s. And dark blue jeans that are a size too big, bought for him to grow into, that are cuffed at the ankles in wide, pale blue bands that exaggerate his weight. His right saddle shoe, tied in a hurry that morning while being hectored by his father from the hallway, is already unraveling.

He is accompanying his parents as they shop for a new house in Pomona, California, after his father has retired from his Army career as an explosives decommissioning expert. Most recently, in North Dakota. The family has never lived longer than a year and a half in any one place. So none of the four siblings have been able to keep friendships, though the youngest is still a baby and has not even started to try. The gentle grown brother and his two bossy sisters are always new to the established school groups. Always new to the walking-distance denominations of church their mother chooses in each place, where she rapidly becomes indispensable. Even though they will leave.

'Neighborhood is neighborhood,' she knows from experience. And each woman will tend each family in times of illness or grief or celebration, with girl children apprenticing along the way. She is always the first to offer a paper plate of her famous chocolate-chip cookies, or a still-warm Tupper-full of chili beans, or biscuits bleeding dark butter-clouds of oil into the bottom of the offered paper bag. This new place is where they will stay and the boy who will become my husband feels an ominous thrill of tempered joy in anticipation.

• • •

They pull up to the curb of a house he loves instantly more than anything he has ever seen in his life, no matter where his father has dragged them. It is dark wood and sage-green stucco and it has a mysterious attic room at its peak like a one-man floor of its own. In the living room, cut-glass windows refract the early light onto Persian rugs that form soft islands on dark wide-plank wood. The house's interior is entrancing to the boy who will become my husband, with deep quiet and light and warmth and calmness enveloping them with as much solidity as the walls that contain them. He has never felt anything like it before.

He wants to live there and cannot breathe for fear of jinxing it. His father is charming the household's mother and the real estate woman and they are laughing and smiling at him. But my husband can sense his mother closing down, as she does in such situations, readying for the inevitable argument that evening when she will accuse him bitterly of being kind and agreeable to everyone but her.

They climb a narrow staircase to the attic room of the one-child family. The boy of the beautiful house is sitting in a flood of light from the windows seen from the street earlier. He is building a model WWII bomber. He finishes carefully laying on a decal before he responds to his mother's introduction.

He is wearing the same t-shirt as the boy who will become my husband and everyone laughs about it, even the boys themselves. The boy of the house is very polite and goes back to his work after saying goodbye. The boy who will become my husband cannot seem to leave the room and has to be coaxed out by the real estate lady.

They tour the small shady backyard where lilacs and irises are still tipped with dew and blankets of violets and moss run between orderly paving stones. My husband will never forget the boy's room, or the aircraft model or the boy or his family or his house, which is summarily dismissed by my husband's mother the minute they get back in the car as lacking the space for a vegetable garden. To which his father, taken aback but recovering, merely says, "Well alright then, mother," which he has called her for as long as my husband can remember. "We'll just find another one then, with more yard. More yard with sun. For your vegetables," and away they drive.

• • •

Two weeks earlier the man who will become my husband has been unexpectedly back-hand slapped, hard, across the face by his father for missing a pitch that his father would have preferred to have been hit out of the field of play. The father spits as he spews his anger and punctuates with further slaps that land unerringly on their target even though he is also holding the steering wheel of a bulky GM station wagon winding widely through the suburban streets.

The slaps are unerring due to their capricious timing. Though eventually all four of his children will come to stand a certain instinctive distance from their father at all times. And when he says, "You know what? I want to talk to you," they will simply turn away and leave the room silent as a cats departing from a patch of sunlight grown dark in the waning of the day.

The following season from the time of the beautiful house his father didn't buy, my husband will excel at baseball due to gaining a few inches in height and a more baseball-appropriate center of balance. Vertical inches gained from his mother's Kentucky-coal-miner cooking with a little Adele Davis added in by then.

After a flash-fire work accident that stops both his smoking habit and his civilian career, my husband's father also stops slapping and begins distance walking; in his one-piece workman's coveralls with a .38 in his pocket because 'the neighborhood has changed.' He begins his walk while it is not yet dawn.

As far as anyone in the family knew, he never shot anybody. Though once my husband was visiting when his father got real excited and said, "Hey. You know what? Come here, I want to tell you something," but my husband was already walking out of the room, so all he heard was the diminishing voice of his father saying, "These blacks walked up to me near the Vons, so I showed 'em the working end of my gun...." Even as my husband sat down in the kitchen with his mom, he could hear his dad asking, "Now, why'd you have to just walk out like that?"

The father took to dumpster diving when he found out he could get three-pound packages of muenster only one day off pull-date in perfect shape. To a boy raised fatherless in the orphanage his mother worked in as a matron, cheese was still a longed-for luxury. Even though the old man he had become had a couple of million in the bank from judicious saving and conservative investing. Back in the days when that was still possible.

My husband's mother died first, of the cancer my husband would come to die of later. After her, his father died, alone in a hospital room in Ontario, California after my husband's sister couldn't abide caring for him anymore. All along the way in those last years each sibling would come to the same place in their thinking. As they beheld the shrunken, powerless, blind and loveless soul who lay there, each would ask themselves, 'How could the monster who made our lives a living hell come down to this, helpless, being?' Who himself could be heard mumbling again and again,

'What am I supposed to do now? How am I supposed to know what to do with myself?'

Outside of Time

The somewhere I long for is not a place but is a moment that reaches out for me and touches me gently, the lightness of touch needing a response before it continues, until touch by touch by touch the asking and the answering are indistinct.

We are children chasing the game before dinner as the streetlights come on in the indigo air. Someone calls "Lights!" and we scatter to our own homes with the secret of our freedoms bolstering our posture as we sit straight at the table. Our hearts are still lit by streetlights and evensong of the pulses within us as we ran the streets.

We never forget these hours as they are our blood and we never forget one another ever-young within us. Where longing is a rule perpetually flowing over a rock into brokenness, into flow, into glint of mica in granite; into metal-smell and chlorine spike traveling.

It cannot catch us we are free we are "It!" We all have won as we scatter and encircle and cannot be lost. We are returning and leaving, we are with our pure-joy, with our shins scratched by the flawless motion of our forwardness.

We are sought by the staid, scared and sad arbiters of correctness who envy us our blisters, our enchanted forgetfulness. Arbiters who long for our hugs scented with metals and earth-roots and wonderment and awe. We are unstoppable even after our growing up. We see the contrails scarring and speaking the sky, we are running the great blue emptiness.

Until touching is itself being touched.

1959, Revelations

The child inside the window
watches things not human
move in the carport:

the strip of wind
that scuttles the dropped
shopping list
across the scored concrete,

the hollow of its
caved chest
lofting its brittle progress along

where the shadow of two crows
swooping up
to drop walnuts

bewilders the old neighbor cat
chasing a long-legged
beetle in the low, spreading light

the redwood bench with
one leaf hanging by a strand
that shelters a spider

in its fragile curvature
where what is ripening
lies protected
within what has died.

The child is young enough
to disregard nothing, sees
the canted light and its
tiny revelations as the formal
scripture of her world,

has not yet forgotten
how to read where
the wind has come from
or the ones it has touched
before her or
after her.

on this day where time splays layered
forgiving and repeating
the lies and the blessings alike

she turns from the sill
tugging a curl of air
with her motion
that then swirls away

turns to the kitchen for an
orange-icing cupcake
to ruin her dinner with
sharing these secrets

only with the baker

an hour before the others
get home
loud, hurried
and irrelevant,
laughing her aside
before leaving her be.

1959, Irene

I was reared in a family of religious iconoclasts. But somehow I myself was born already religious, with a tendency to imagine towards the Big Picture.

Even to this day for me there is a palpable, deep and direct connection to saying the Lord's Prayer on my knees on the floor at the bed of the black house-keeper who essentially reared me from one to nine years old, and the backyard explorer/scientist/monk I was as a child. In a temporal reverse, that old-soul of a young girl who I was still firmly holds my heart the way a child's hand is held while crossing a busy, dangerous street. Undiminished by my long years.

It was in the backyard that I first discovered texture and temperature, physical ability and volition; that I first perceived a child's-mind basic pedagogy of physics, geology, botany and where I first clearly knew the uniting carrier of all of those things, later to be named for me as God.

Being taught the Lord's Prayer by Irene, after I asked what she was doing and saying on her knees at the side of her bed (because like any very young child I was all over the house always watching and asking questions for which I had no reservoir for receiving the answers), she said it was prayer and asked me if

I wanted to learn it? I got on my knees and she instructed me to put my elbows on the mattress and my palms together. Over time I learned the words.

But of course, that as-yet small reservoir meant that incoming knowledge and experience got mixed up in the process of ingestion. So that "Our Father" became my deceased father who in reality was everywhere in conversation during my upbringing and perhaps had been explained to my child inquiries as "in Heaven." And we literally lived in the part of LA that was called Hollywood (then a lower-middle-class neighborhood of struggling performers) and my father had been a successful film director even with a star on Hollywood Boulevard, so "hallowed," a word inconceivable to me, became "Hollywood" to cover all those bases.

"Thy kingdom come, Thy will be done..." became my heart's yearning reality for my continuing father in absentia compared to all my friends' fathers who ran the show on site. And in my version of him he was all-forgiving and never anything less than a supportive and loving being. Unlike some of the fathers I heard about in my friends' realities, sometimes it seemed kinder to have an imaginary one. Everything was there except the man himself, so when I misunderstood "Hollywood" in Irene's instruction the world became clear.

Perhaps needless to point out, I had a very early tilt towards abstraction coupled with limited concrete proofs and I ran with it. So that's where both religion and writing set their first roots in me. Essentially, where the world provided too few explanations, or clearly talked-down or inadequate ones, I found local proofs and explanations that I preferred – made up from the evidence around me.

I suspect many people have these child-like conceptual underpinnings and each of us more or less modifies, or carries, these enchanted and hope-filled ontogenies through to adulthood editing as we go.

That my specific late father was right there with me in the backyard as I concluded that the dried-out and splayed-open weed inflorescences of summer were just like Fourth of July sparklers. That from the randomly distributed dirt made up of blacks and greys and gentle browns, the sparrows and hooded juncos rose as animated expressions of the earth to scratch for seeds and tiny pebbles. That cumulus clouds were the giant dogs, alligators and plush stuffed toys of an uber-world without rules, were scudding and shifting at will free of pummeling big brothers and bed-time schedules, forced baths and my exhausted, lonely mother's dark and unpredictable moods.

Perhaps that's where My Father was, up in the limitless transparent blue of Hollywood if that was what heaven was and perhaps he was watching from there and here simultaneously, spending time with me, taking care of me. Irene and the Lord's Prayer basically connected the dots in my child mind and relieved me of needing to buy into the destructively unpredictable flailing world of my immediate family. The calm engendered by that became essential to my well-being.

From there my religious reaching started: I began to beg to go home to Watts with Irene on weekends and when she would be given permission (and I'm sure, paid), she would bring me along with her to her Jehovah's Witness meetings; began to attend my best friend's Catholic Church on Sundays where I would put my mother's given single quarter into a donation envelope; explored my father's late '40s-abandoned Jewish rituals with a beloved high school friend's welcoming family at Hanukkah; began reading Buddhist teachings in high school and took formal Bodhisattva vows to commit to the practice that lasts to this day.

All of which began with the misunderstood concept of "my Father" and "Hollywood" and their many meanings and societal powers. The reverent acceptance and inclusion exhibited in The Lord's Prayer and those many religious rituals I shared became for me the actual meaning of the word "hallowed." And it has consecrated all that began in that little backyard scientist/monk's heart and continued through my life of education, marriage, child-rearing and still-flowing faith.

As has Irene's down-on-the-floor, lifetime-lasting compassion and patience toward this flailing, exhausted and moody world that has become our cultural family.

1961, Assembly Required

Even now I see my mother from below, looking up. As if I am still sitting on the edge of the closed toilet seat by the sink in my cut-offs keeping her company early on a weekday summer morning.

She stands there spot-lit doing her make-up before work. I am a terribly skinny nine years old with no hint of womanliness any time soon. I am ominously pensive, a demeanor that all my life will pull people in or push people away at a glance. She is thirty-five, mother of one daughter and two older sons. She is already a widow of eight long years' duration. She is voluptuous, spilling over with primary, contagious, slightly nervous sexual energy that draws everyone toward her. Though from close enough, watched long enough, her light-brown eyes will betray an irrepressible shadow of soul, a muted but anchoring ill-ease.

This morning I am studying her. All day I study everything like a little scientist, in great detail, for its working way: bugs, my brothers, myself, our housekeeper Irene, my mother. She is 'putting on her face' before her job as a secretary in the legal department of CBS. She has hiked her tapered skirt-hem up above her knees, Marilyn Monroe-style, so she can 'breathe.' She has renamed herself Vanessa, lately of Hollywood, California, née Minadora of Hammond, Indiana via immigrant parents from Transylvania, Romania. She is an inventor of herself, trained as an actress who loves to point out that she is a gypsy. Compared to her, I am already a little monk, a killjoy for unadorned reality.

This morning as I study her my mother runs a weak trickle of hot water from the tap. It curls like a molten silver rope and steams, smelling of minerals and pot metal. She removes her tiny Maybelline brush from its little red drawer in its little plastic case, and after swiping it across the scalding water, scruffs it in the black block of mascara. With exaggeratedly wide-open eyes, she thickens her already ample lashes. Then with her eyes still hugely wide open as though they are stuck that way, she slowly turns to stare at me watching her, eye-brow arching high, left eye narrowing. Her Béla Lugosi gag. I laugh. She nods slowly with a contained, triumphant, smile: gotcha!

During our morning ritual, we rarely speak, we listen. She feels a little uncomfortable around me, I do not give her enough of the response she craves. She says shocking things to get a rise out of me, or does her tragic, giant lost child rendition of Lenny from "Of Mice and Men," or a hunched-up, terror-struck Peter Lorre from "The Beast with Five Fingers." I smile, or laugh, but usually stay inside myself. She is aware of this, yet often we are good shared company and this day we feel unified, each of us in our separate way.

Today she smiles as I watch her, proud to be teaching me her ways: how to assemble a beautiful face. As it will turn out, in a long life, I will come to wear make-up only rarely. Yet I will always find the rituals of *doing* make-up, the way the tiny precious containers click open and closed, their intimate close-up mirrors for one, the bright light required, each substance's identifying perfume and at last, the transformation – wishing I could stand the feel of the finalized mask on my skin, the exciting social manipulation of its effect.

The sound of my brothers fighting drifts up from the downstairs kitchen – the exchange a series of angry verbal jabs, then the sound of a heavy blunt object hitting some wooden furniture. My mother facially ignores this with a motionless deep sigh, never pausing her brush. A neighbor starts her Chevy and force-warms it, revving up in a long, breathy mechanical growl then jerks it impatiently into reverse. There is a screech of tires from the street, then a horn. My mother looks at me and shakes her head, rolls her eyes at the flawed world she and I are immured from. A scrub jay near our window sends a rasping chirr to its mate, who replies from further up the hill.

My mother has progressed from face cream to foundation to eyeliner; from eyeliner to mascara to rouge brushed on with a wide, sable brush, an expensive indulgence. She suddenly brushes my nose with it to make me smile, but I am already tired of her teasing and don't respond. She is still in her curlers, which finally she undoes in order to tease her hair high and round, finishing with strategic wisps that emphasize her eyes and graceful neckline.

Lastly lipstick, then she rotates a pencil liner in place to emphasize the pale mole just above her top lip, á la Marilyn. She then stabilizes the whole effort with what seems like several minutes of hairspray. It fills the bathroom with a roiling cloud of sweet, sticky chemical droplets. I cover my mouth and breathe through my fingers, scrunching down my eyelids to slits. She laughs at me, blinking tears from her own irritated eyes, frowning at my hopeless sobriety.

For the price of beauty, the completed woman is a wonder of presentation: arched Elizabeth-Taylor eyebrows, tender, depth-implying Monroe eye-shadow; wind-swept thoroughbred Barbara Walters bangs. Lovely, dewy, attention-getting, attention-giving; energetic, sexy, sophisticated. Vanessa!

Vanessa. My mother who left the soot-covered Indiana steel-milling town of her birth and childhood and what she considered her no-longer appropriate Romanian name, Minadora, meaning 'gift of the moon,' behind. My mother, who worked in said steel-mills to save up to send herself to acting school in Chicago for two years. Moved to LA to make her career, met my father while working as a hatcheck girl at Chasen's, fell in love and got pregnant right away, her nineteen to his forty. Married and bore him three children before he died at forty-six.

In the whole life I know her, she will never formally act. And yet until the evening before the day she dies — forty years hence from that summer morning in nineteen sixty-one, she will never stop acting. But by then, I am so used to these characterizations of hers that when she drops them in earnest, the last hour of our relationship on earth, I will fully fail to notice – having so rarely ever seen the woman she really was.

II.

1986, Beginning in Stride

Our first date is in Westwood Village where I've grown up and gone to college. The man who will become my husband's back is to the outside wall of the cafe patio and I am facing him. He orders coffee and when it comes with a small bowlful of tiny plastic tubs of Coffee Mate he insists to the waitress that he needs real cream. But he insists gently and she finds a way to comply.

He pours the thick white liquid into the coffee and it bounces off the bottom of the cup and up again to form cumulous clouds that roll luxuriantly up to the dark surface, coloring it like a camel hair coat. I order red wine.

As I tell my birth-to-now history he drinks cup after cup of coffee and orders more cream. He watches my eyes and my person with such enthusiasm that even I begin to be impressed with myself!

He is on his sixth refill when he begins his own story and I listen carefully and interrupt him here and there for details, digging in: how long ago was this divorce? Why did they divorce? I can see both the discomfort and enthusiasm in his face that anyone would bother to care for these details.

We begin with these two hours but over the years our stories unfurl backwards and forwards for decades gaining details. Until sweetly they submerge into the silences of simple shared knowing.

1987, One a.m.

Moon reaching white
long-stemmed
chrysanthemums,
petals splayed
drinking
reflected
light.

1988

Early in our marriage, living in an old apartment down the hill from Griffith Park, two men came to the back door of the kitchen while we were cooking dinner inside. For some reason, the door had been left unlocked.

I was near the pantry by the door when one of the men opened it, stupefied on some drug but aggressive and fast with his blond buddy behind him pushing in. I called my husband's name in such abject fear that he read the situation immediately. He simply stepped in front of the half-opened door, grabbed the knob, preventing them from entering further, and said, "Get out of here! Get the hell out of here!" He dismissed them with such force of determination that they backed out in a panic, the one in front making the one in back fall and grab the one in front so then they both fell, rolled back to standing reaching up towards the night darkness, then ran like hell.

My husband had been utterly unafraid of them. He just made them go away through conviction and presence. So very gentle a man but with a strength so deep his surface showed only a trace of the current beneath. Only the weak or distracted missed this in him. Or doubted it for long.

1992, Ojai

We rent a house on an untamed acre in far eastern Ojai. My husband drives to LA daily so we can live all the way out there – an insane commute, possibly cruel. But he professes to love listening to music, both ways, all the way, and not to mind traffic – so it seems somewhat acceptable. We both loved the place so.

One night as he drives home along the winding and rising narrow two-lane highway a driver begins tailgating him perilously close with his bright lights on. It's several tense miles of this until there's a pull-out that my (very patient but by now alarmed) husband can take to get out of the way and allow the driver to pass.

Only when no one passes him and he pulls back onto the road does he realize it actually was a brilliant full moon on his tail seeming to disappear and rise again over and over as my husband ascended the hilly road.

As it turned out, all along in those first years there were many ways it was hard to tell what was really going on. But slowly we all just blended in with the raw beauty of the environment, took things as they came, and hoped for the best.

During working hours on weekdays it was just our son and I — and the coyotes and bobcats. Once, through the kitchen window while doing dishes, I saw a full-grown cougar run through the open gate and our yard out to the barranca that was the western border of the property. He was huge, graceful, unconcerned, utterly feral. Suddenly there, suddenly gone.

Our son remembers this later as my having left him in the car strapped in his car seat with the windows open as the cougar ran by him. I remember it as our first week there as he, an infant, played safely at my feet on the kitchen floor.

To me the sighting was a warning of sorts: never let our son play outside alone until he was old enough to be aware. He remembers it as an abandonment of sorts, leaving him vulnerable to a wild animal as I observed from the safety of the house.

Our two memories are irresolvable.

Even with its beauty (and wild animals), it was kind of a lonely place to be. So our family began to keep canaries to break up what felt like our city-folks' isolation. We kept each one unmated so it would sing for us, making our way through three of them over several years, until finally we realized we would become too attached to them to get any more once the last one died.

We listened to the wind and the rare car passing by. Occasionally a neighbor rode by on horseback.

At the end of the day I would bathe our son and his father would arrive home a bit after seven p.m. In cool weather I would have built a hearth fire for my husband to light. Then our sweet son would stand in front of it fresh from his bath, let his towel fall away in the warmth and eat an ice cream bar for dessert – cool, hot, cold. Then his father would put him to bed.

Or if his dad was going to be late arriving home, I would do so – read to him in the forest-scene up-holstered couch and then sing to him, Amazing Grace or He's Got The Whole World with person-alized variations until he drifted off.

There was a baby-monitor in his room just by his crib and near the window where a great horned owl would routinely call from the high branches of the eucalyptus tree outside.

One night we listened by the fireplace through the baby monitor as the owl called "Who? Who? Who?" and our son, not even a year old, answered in kind, fully asleep, "Who? Who? Who?" already acclimated to the country – night predators and all.

At a year old our son learned to run before he learned to walk and thereafter the years of his child-hood rush joyously and precariously by in kind.

1998, Death of the Last Caged Canary

It begins and ends with silence.
Carried only once,
you are lighter than air.

In our backyard ritual,
a circle of children,
we are the first religion.

Incantations of
yearning and recognition
stagger upward,
unaccustomed to the sky.

A draft rustles your feathers
and I see you, head tucked,
on a branch on your island:

where there you dream
the dream without hunger,
and just off the map
you are home.

2010, Our Son's Room

I am sitting on the edge of the bed in our son's old room. Every day I look for someplace new in the house as though there is a hidden door somewhere or as if I am in one of the dreams I have so often where I find a staircase I have simply overlooked for years that leads to a whole new wing.

Our son's room always feels new, especially as he comes and goes from college imbued with his mysterious adventures. Sometimes he stays here for a few days and then he is off again, for weeks or months.

When he's not here, his room doubles as the guest room and his dad or I can be a guest if we need someplace new to stay for a few hours. My husband is sleeping here now after cataract surgery and the room is full of woozy gratefulness that all went well. Pale afternoon light seeps in between the windy tree branches outside that dance with long-legged afternoon shadows.

I am sitting on the bed next to him, keeping him company. But he has fallen asleep mid-sentence holding my hand on his heart.

I don't want to wake him so I just sit face-to-face with our son's pendulum clock on the wall opposite.

The one he and his dad salvaged for our son's child-hood clock-collecting hobby — too expensive to fix, too unique to pass up, its glass missing, face open to the air.

It has only one hand in a serendipitous time-riff on the famous Zen koan, and that one hand within the otherwise empty face rests at twenty-one. So twenty-four times a day it is exactly on time, no winding, no ticking, no specific hour. Our son might like to fix it when he's older after some return to his solitary child concentration. Later he might even sit bent over it protectively as an old-fashioned accounting of the great vastness.

Will he have his father's patient heart? His vigilance? Will he be sounding his youth, like an echo? I'll save it for him, just in case.

But at the moment he is eighteen and so full of life that when he must sit, his drummer's hands and at least one other part of his body taps a quick beat, not nervous, just miraculously rapid. With his foot in its perennial tennis shoe on the floor or with his hands on the table or with his tongue against the roof of his mouth or all four simultaneously in entrancing revolving counter-times.

He is already complex beyond my understanding and when he is here I can hear the compelling sound of him from any room I'm in — his cadence gentle and rapid like a moth held near the ear.

While he is away my husband and I are mostly quiet here, in an attentive peace readjusting to one another. Our individual endeavors are more impor-

tant to us, as when we were our son's age; our to-
getherness more intense, as before he came into our
lives. Each of us listening to the separate sounds of
our paired future.

Here in this room, in this unaccountable hour,
time does not seem to be moving at all. The palm
tree across the street, visible through the window, is
slowly swaying in a rougher, unpredictable wind high
above the ground currents. Every now and then one
of its dry feathery leaves lifts and trembles then settles again against its spiky trunk.

My husband's hand eventually uncurls, releasing
me as he enters deep sleep. I feel his strong heartbeat
on the back of my fingers as I slip my hand from under his.

I leave the room with careful quiet steps to begin
cooking dinner. In case he's hungry when he wakes.

2010, Practice

I am driving my Buddhist monk teacher back to the temple through the chaparral forest at night. Mile after mile along the two-lane mountainous road we travel through pitch dark, rarely passing another vehicle. Our car's headlights are rigid triangular beams jerkily cutting into the flexible surround of black. Beyond their plane of illumination the hills roll up from the road to the star-flecked sky and down away from it into precipitous canyons. At this hour the forest is animated with the searches of hungry nocturnal animals, their smaller prey hiding in the shadows-within-shadows under the scrub brush.

Through the slightly open window many night-cool scents weave into the car's warmed air like black ink unfurling into clear water: coastal sage, hot tires on dusty asphalt, yerba buena, motor oil, dew-infused rye grass.

I glance briefly at my teacher, the two of us softly revealed by reflected dashboard light. She is a distinctive woman, just sixty, statuesque and fair of face. Her compelling appearance is further distilled by monastic robes, shaven head and formal bearing. Several empty earring holes pierce her lobes, attesting to her former lay life in Amsterdam.

Calmly and slowly she turns successive wooden beads of a rosary between her thumb and forefinger, silent in sympathetic sway with the vehicle. I know she is protecting us with her meditation.

I tell her about a friend who says that to dream a dream many times means that you're trying to work something out. But to dream a dream only once is prescient. I tell her about the dream of the red pickup truck, how, suddenly there it is, braked, in front of me in traffic and I am going too fast to stop. I wake up at the unrevealed moment of the inevitable, soaked in sweat, shaking, terrified. I tell my teacher that now I am afraid to drive this road, that I am always on the lookout for the red pickup.

"Well then," my teacher says and pauses. "Don't *be* afraid. Be *careful*."

2010, Walking Meditation

bird tracks
on the sand
of the incense bowl
at the foot
of a Bodhisattva

the scent of irrigation
on the dusty parched air

the burning inexorable sun
magnified by low clouds
impatient to hasten fall

far out in the field
where it is silent
but for tractors
        and prayers

there is one small
tatter of a flag
and on it an upward curve
of bright ink

always the invitation
of your kind smile
in the small things
that only children find for play

2011, The Arbor

After the arbor grapes have ripened
the vine's leaves turn brown and fall,
each one a wordless eloquent page
with its days of light and fruition
written brittle upon it,

each one a map with roads faded
directions only a vague sense of things

fallen downward where
the gentlest touch breaks them
footsteps shatter them
yet daily I net them from the pool
where some of them float
each one eloquent
spinning on the water's surface

as though delighted, as though
itself winding the breeze —
a cup of sky, a Chinese junk, a wizened
ballerina, her head tilted to the sun
her arms thin as paper
her shadows repeating her dance
on the water's reflective surface

the heart of her being
itself to teach the wind
to hold,
to carry, to obey
unending change
as joy

2011, The Hours Themselves

It seems late in my husband's illness, but it's hard to know. Perhaps I'm just exhausted from straddling hope and inevitability; tired from balancing his remarkable endurance against the statistical forebodings. It's hard for me to know exactly where to exist – here in these languid hours of caring and closeness? Or out there, somewhere else in time, where my future exists unmoored from this man I have spent every day intertwined with for half the years of my life.

One night I have a compelling dream. I have dived to the bottom of an Olympic-sized pool that is all one depth, about twenty-five feet. I feel sure I have enough air to make it back to the surface, but only just enough. The water is a profound limpid blue, its pressure immense.

In the dream, I am the painfully slender young girl of my childhood. But my mind is the elder woman I am now. As I swim I realize that this is what I want to do with my life, to wrestle with the deep water, over and over, just like this. To struggle with it and to strengthen myself against it. I remember the dream many times over the months: my skinny arms; the water seamlessly hollowing itself to my form; the oscillating yellow-white surface glinting above me.

Today my husband comes into my study as I am working. He lies down on the narrow guest bed on the fresh white sheets in the heat. Held by the cool surface, as he naps, his blue jeans and shirt billow over the angular form of his depleted body: his broad shoulder bones; his sharp hip; the hard fold of his long arms attenuated by his lean hands and fingers. His round knees are wider than his thighs or calves. He breathes deeply and slowly, utterly within himself.

In his sleep, turning to his other side, he groans with the effort and the unyielding firmness of the mattress. I cannot think about where we are lest I begin sinking and lose sight of the sweet surface: being together on a summer day; the fan whirring and cranking; the house finches just outside the door stringing their melodies out along the fabric of wind; the compression of the hours themselves, transparent, fleeing unencumbered.

2012, Shift

My husband is up on time this morning: four a.m. He is setting out to do, again, exactly what he set out to do yesterday: drive to his beloved dentist in Korea Town, eighty miles south-east of here, for an eight o'clock appointment. Driving is the last thing he can imagine giving up. But yesterday traffic got the best of him and he turned back. Today is another set of variables.

His energy is good, his movements as he gets dressed are purposeful and elegant, turning his t-shirt right-side-out with both hands, tossing it up, quickly, then threading his right hand into the first sleeve-hole while it is still mid-air; his left hand through the second sleeve-hole before it has time to settle on his waist. He straightens the shirt on his hips while closing the folding closet door. He is something to watch. All his anger of the day before transformed to precision and purpose.

The bath tub is still warm from his bathing in the dark, splashes of water still blooming into the rough Saltillo tiles. The room smells soap-sweet and breathes a warm moisture back into me.

My husband remembers everything this morning, efficiently, even as I, still in bed, am curling away from his bright wakefulness: to take his first eight pills; to put his syringe into the car for later; to take the list of all his chemo drugs for the dental hygienist to consider; to note the type and dose of his blood thinner as he calls it. I worry for a short moment about the hours he will spend on the freeway, about what could happen if he has an accident and bleeds uncontrollably.

I imagine myself with him, holding his wound with my hand, willing clearings in the traffic so the ambulance can get through, quickly explaining my husband's special circumstances to the EMT, just in time to save his life.

I turn my mind away from these catastrophic-imaginings-within-catastrophe because they lead to me sitting in a chair unable to remember why I'm sitting there. Instead I insist to my thoughts that they remember the continuous flux of everything, the whole breathing ellipsis of benign possibility in which we all surge in kind. It is the only thing I know for sure, yet always I have to remind myself to remember.

It is my only prayer.

Later I hold my first cup of coffee. Face-by-face and car-by-car I let my thoughts let go of the traffic jam as if calming myself with a shawl in a sudden fall chill. I rise from the chair to open the shoji screens, watch the hillside chaparral exhale its spicy and shocking white clouds into the deep morning blue sky. I let go only just enough to walk across the room, and then I too am in the flow again.

Brand new clouds, traveling.

· · ·

My husband has lost seventy-five pounds, which would leave some men dead, or bragging. But instead it leaves this man like a spark off a hearth fire: lithesome, agile, his steps lightly anchored in an astonishing restless balance — moving, shifting. He is already gone from me and in his place is this new man, distant, glinting, who only suddenly remembers I am here in the room with him.

He says, "Thank you! Thank you!" while grabbing my face so urgently and awkwardly that it makes us both laugh. Then, he says, "Thank you. Thank you," holding tighter still to make me remember and remember.

He has shed much of what is cumbersome to him: his uncomfortable way of sitting in a chair, the many confined gestures that linger from a childhood of brutal fathering. Now he drapes himself across the cushions and settles in completely, long-limbed and pensive, laughing occasionally to himself. Where before he would talk and talk, watching sideways for response, now I have to ask.

"What are you thinking?"

"It's a strange thing," he replies. "To be dying and feel more alive than ever," leaning toward me, amazed and amazing.

2012, Entropy

The vigilant house finches
planted them:
giant sunflowers by day
heads bowed in the late-summer heat, leaves
yellowed with parch and mold. By night
mendicants – patient, humbling.

Inside transformation, she hesitates:
unable to wake or sleep
making her to-do list
by moon light among the plundering raccoons.

One season sees another yet cannot touch it,
July's full moonlight
a map of autumn's high noon.
When is not a question
light asks of space.
The day birds
ceaselessly kick through the leaves
hunching, scattering.

The morning after a dinner party
we stare at the sink full of dirty
dishes, the ruination of the kitchen,

"Start with just one dish,"
my husband teases me, waiting there
with a dry clean dish towel
too kind to laugh. He is patient
where I am not; he easily accepts
where I stand firm, bargaining.

When our child was born,
we wound our hours
around his growing form, turning
shadow and light toward this
cardinal love. Where

does it go? I ask, here now, he
is here now, he is gone now, they
were there then, where am I?

Inside transformation, my own dissolution,
scratching memory into the night soil —
one leaf at a time, one seed at a time.

2012, Diverging

He works at home now in the back garage where his computer desk shares space with the washer/dryer in the opposite corner of the large room. I am here now and he is enjoying the interruption of my presence. My side is to him, and he watches me shake and toss each piece of laundry into the open washer.

He has said he is captivated by my hands, has been for all these decades now. Even when I'm angry, my staccato gestures stabbing the air, I can see that he has ceased listening, so distracted as he is by my gestures. Yet I cannot stop myself. All along he has only been watching my hands, mute pugilists in their empty little duel with the air.

But now my thought-filled, repetitive gestures with the laundry move peacefully in concert as I take in all the patterns and colors of our clothing. He knows I consider this one of my domestic meditations as I would call it. He thought perhaps I said that to console myself in this increasingly continuous state of caring for him since his illness was named fatal.

He is incredibly grateful that the arguing has stopped, their misdirected and hurtful striving for position with one another. It's very simple now. Work. Food. Pain-fighting. Sleep. Infusions. Broken only by the mechanical hum of their long hours of driving on the freeway to treatment. My determination to keep him alive as he sleeps in the passenger seat in his favorite curled position holding the morning sun's warmth on his hip and shoulders as I drive and drive.

Now we are falling away from one another and have never been closer. Like the leaves on the ground or his beloved birds at the feeder. Impersonal in an odd way yet married in purpose, in time, and in union in our love of our son.

My Christian husband now is profoundly glad for Jesus, who will hold him later. Forever. His robes so thin and yet perfectly warm. The Mystery will hold him, as I have. But that is going to be later. After he surrenders completely and lets the churn in his blood take him down.

He isn't ready for that yet. There is too much to do. He'll stay for as long as he can, whatever he can manage. There is just too much to do yet. And never to waste even a minute with his beloved son.

He watches me toss in the oversized red plaid flannel pj's I used to look cute in back when I was younger and slender. Now they exaggerated my overweight. He wonders if he will be able to find me, after. If he will be able to watch me in my life, walking in the yard. Doing only my own laundry, my hands and their rhythm moving through the air without his presence to witness them.

He turns away from his computer to the sunlight. I go to him and hold one side of his face with my hand and kiss him (how unutterably thin he is, I think, how remarkably handsome still) and as he turns to look at me with his melancholy thoughts still shadowing his eyes, my kiss lands off-kilter to his lips.

I laugh and he faces me full-on, and to me it looks as though he has returned from some far, far away place. As though he has to reorient himself to rediscover my presence.

"Awkward," I laugh again with a question flickering over my eyes. I frown, then will it away, in an instant. He sees it, notes it, lets it pass.

We kiss straight on, lightly, familiar, slowly and for a long while. Then he says, "Gotta get back," and as he turns to his computer the screen throws a cold, white-blue cast onto his face.

I turn to him again and he is back to watching the sunlight in the yard, still as a hummingbird briefly resting on a high branch. Transfixed by something I cannot see.

Moon

just now
as the neighborhood dogs
call morning, (the same way
they call evening), simply to call
simply to anyone

the waning moon
sinks into the shade
of the horizon trees

(the same way
it sinks
into infinite space)
giving its light
indifferently, generously

and even with the ragged edge
cut from its fullness
remembers its gladness,
holds, in fact

both aspects, one
its immutable face, one
its unwavering motion

2012, Verge

Now my husband has rediscovered model building. At first he just orders kit after kit from Amazon, and special task lights with magnifying lenses of various sizes, secreting the growing tower of boxes in the garage, also his successful business's workspace. But it turns out to be mostly too dark for model work back there, or only spot lit with tensor lamps inadequate for the job.

So I fix up a place in the family room under one of the oversized skylights in our house. Here is where the sunlight streams in most generously and also where a long, wide-planked dining table that has taken, of late, to gathering abandoned paperwork and odd objects, seems better suited to my husband's presence and purposes. One day I clear it and wax it and ask him if he'd like to come in and he says, "Sure! Yeah. This is nice."

It is warm here and filled with the various shifting sounds of our household. We are a one-child family, though our "child," a boy, is a man now, coming and going as he pleases. It is calm and loving and a sense of expansive time as wide as the sky just outside the French doors lends its roaming-ness to the room as if we were up on a high vantage.

The tower of small and flimsy cardboard model kit boxes and my husband move in to work here and in the late afternoons we sit together. I am reading or thinking about what to cook for dinner in the armchair nearby, and he is working on his models, holding up a tiny decal for me to admire or mixing colors from small glass bottles of paint, just the same as they were in the '50s.

More and more often he forgets I'm there with him and I can tell he's off somewhere, alone with his thoughts. I just watch him then and fill myself with his presence. I hold the fear at bay where it shivers, like a harmless guard-fence current of electricity in my chest.

And it is so very quiet here, even with the music on, loud.

2012, Fear of the Dark

My husband was never afraid of death. It was not-life that shook him; not-life he snubbed with incessant work and ritual evening margaritas; not-life towards which he strode with furious accession as if toward an unfair disciplinarian who held a whip in her hand. Strode forward, but would not meet her eye.

She won.

Of course. She won.

2012, Bier

I wonder at the glass bead
I find on your desk
marked, "Imagine,"
whether to include it
on your bier;

I hold it, then conclude that
imagining is of this, living, realm
and that now
you don't need it.
Now that you are all possibility.

I include instead

the small slightly-burned candles
from your crowded final birthday party,
lighted only long enough
to sing the celebratory song
all voices blending;
a love note folded into
an origami seed packet;
a set of drumsticks from our
son for your rhythm, changing;

a gold foil candy wrapper from Argentina,
things from our last days;
homegrown rosemary and kumquats;

the last of the bandages
you no longer suffer to wear;
a cookie fortune, "You have a natural grace and
great consideration for others," so true and
in which we all basked
simply to be in your presence;

thoughts of: the drift of sea fog that day,
a dog barking;
a walnut in its shell
dropped by the crows whose cunning
you so admired; a copy of the
animal funeral you delivered to the
local unlucky squirrels so often; a ticket
you saved from the Thievery concert
you attended with our son
before we knew. A prescription from the oncologist;

infinite invisible spreading love;

homegrown black sage; sal spreader sage, tridentate,
invisible scent drifting everywhere;
no more pain; no more deadlines
high cirrus clouds traveling fast,
stars visible through the branches as they move.

2012

He used to roll up my sleeves for me. He would do this carefully, snapping each cuff tight as he went. Smoothing each new layer to make sure the accumulating folds weren't bulky or pulling on the body of the shirt as I raised my arms. As he worked, so very quietly and seriously, I would think of his military father, his 1950s soldier-on mother, his three younger siblings. The whole unit, his family, moving from place to place as his father was re- and re-assigned. Rarely having enough time to make friends. Sisters for playmates and a mother for a father. A flurry of strong women oddly dominated by, but absent of, men.

Each time my husband would efficiently make taut a fold of my sleeve it sounded like a flag snapping in a high wind somewhere, its ring-nut tolling an irregular counterpoint against the pole: in a school yard; or approaching a courthouse; or transiting a vast cemetery lawn.

As he rolled each sleeve I would hold my arm still, slightly away from my body. His cool fingers would lightly graze my skin as they reached in to smooth the fabric. I would eventually laugh at this even though he was so serious with his task. But he would continue, unchanged, concentrating. I would say, "That tickles." He would say, "Love you Jem," and keep folding. Somehow I never knew what he was thinking even though I knew he was loving me.

Now that he's gone, I roll my own sleeves. It's easier to do before I put the shirt on, so I stand in the slight morning chill with the shirt laid out flat on the bed: folding, snapping, smoothing the shirt-sleeves. And I listen to the only thing I know absolutely that we still share: the silence of the room, its open emptiness.

III.

2017, LAX Rush Hour

with pockets-full of irrelevant euros
you emerge through the crowd
as if all-at-once –
famished, tired and restless,

cheeks flushed
with love and nascent jet-lag;
thoughts of the return to common weekdays
already cinching your brows;

you ask to be taken to in-&-out
where the flash-bright light and
midnight fried potatoes mottle
your young complexions,

and the eating tires you
so that the rush of your stories slows
and hushes
only just as I can begin to imagine it –

Paris,
in winter,
in love;

in the back seats of the car you resist
but finally give in and nod off
as if in a fairy-tale
falling towards each other
even while belted apart;

I watch you in the rear-view while
braking through mad LA traffic
as if chauffeuring an aspect of miracle
safely to its appointed fate;

when we get there you pull
your luggage and each other
whispering gratefully to bed;

and I sit for a while
by the wood-filled hearth fire –
too tired to light it,
to enchanted to sleep

2019, It's All Good

I knit as she sleeps, even in this low light intended to keep her gentled. Simple rows of garter stitch that I don't need much careful sight for and that allow me to listen for her breathing, still uneven at six weeks old. Some breaths are so quiet I can barely perceive them so I walk over and hover until I see her abdomen rising and falling quickly. Some breaths are deep and greedy as though she is remembering recent immersion's effortless oxygen. Perhaps dreaming of her protected world within her mother where their heartbeats mysteriously wove in and out of phase. A nine-month duet as her consciousness opened like a flower.

I first met her when she was only hours old and already she was bunching and flexing in the new gravity, her eyes shadowy and open, tracking light and blinking. Her whole being gently and momentously surging with curiosity. She is my brand-new granddaughter. I am her brand-new grandmother. It's been a while since I've been brand-new! Unexpected miracles all around.

When this very local miracle entered our world everything else tumbled and danced into new positions like leaves in a sudden warm wind. Its sound compellingly familiar, beyond words or meaning.

Still. I worry a bit.

About this world she's coming into. But my son and most of his friends keep saying, "It's all good." I used to answer, "Well, maybe not in Kabul, or Florida. Or even Thousand Oaks for that matter." But they'd just laugh at my 1950s mental-habit of darkness and wander away. Just done with me for the moment. I used to think this "It's all good" was some dismissive millennial verbal tic, something like the '80s "Don't worry; be happy," sung on a beach between sunscreen slatherings. But far from it.

They are *too* well-aware of the generosity of risks here and their dire implications. "It's all good," isn't a set of blinders, it's a cultural incantation. It's a prayer. The battle-cry of an army of the muscled, energized, imaginative future itself heard long before you see them coming over the hill.

I admire my two and their brave, beautiful, vulnerable baby. Every human emotion passes across her face, one reaction easily overtaking another without intention or manipulation. Their future won't be easy, no future ever has been, nor any present. I take them out to dinner and I listen to their rushed words even as I wonder what they are thinking. Their humor is so dark; their hope so luminous. Their strained patience with the old is taut with righteous energy not wasted on resentment.

They've ducked their heads to rush into the torrent more efficiently, unintimidated. Holding each other and the baby tight to them. Putting the most egregious of the past away all the lighter to travel. And to make room for joy.

My simple knitting stitches loop and gather one-by-one as I slip them off of bamboo needles. Now she is breathing in that huffing kind of way she does just before she starts crying, gathering her energy for a magnificent protest. Hunger? Hygiene? Temperature? Unnamed pain? A list of needs paralleling the news headlines.

There she lies, a generation in her own right emerging by tiny urgent degrees. Her left eyebrow cinches slightly, almost a frown! Her limbs bunch then reach out — still, sleep reclaims her and she quiets, her little fists holding emptiness for the moment, the place-holder of all potential.

When her parents walk in she has woken and smiles as her mom receives her to feed — wants to begin crying again, but her mom coos her quiet and directs her to a breast. It *is* all good: her little fists still filled with emptiness; her eloquent fingers one-by-one slowly learning to unfurl.

2020, The Fluidity of Fate

The first several nights here I have no belongings yet. Only the cat, a change of clothes, a portable sleeping pad I place beneath windows with no curtains, an extra blanket near me for the cat to have a recognizable scent-place by my side.

In a two-month epiphany to be near my 13-month-old granddaughter I've dismantled everything, sold my house, bought a new one and driven a whole day north, away from my life's history, the home where my late husband and I made our family, the organic garden we tended for eighteen years that bore every delicious fruit we could think of planting.

Now, lying here in an empty room, I can hear the freeway nearby, the ubiquitous prolonged motorcycle roars, local barking dogs and in the quiet between, the occasional shy-seeming bird settling in, calling out to her companions in the safety of our shared shadows.

Everything else is silence and the unfamiliar walls staring me down with their history of love and conflict, intention and entropy, risk and hope – the failing and renewable energies of a life. Big, little; big, little; big, little.

What is there to do but let go and dream? To remember the story of shared hours; imagine more; reach out across the floor to stroke the shaken cat only just now released from so many hours in a cage in the unfathomable car.

On the floor we seem to be sharing continuous ground with the tree roots, our companions with reaching branches clothed only in the sheer moonlight of an early waxing crescent.

Late silence and the heady implications of what I have done to have begun a new life overwhelmingly emptied of the beloved and familiar, refilled entirely of possibility.

● ● ●

My granddaughter has been here all day, eating, running, pushing my body away from the sink to hold her, read to her, play blocks with her and do the stuffed animal dialogue for her, "Giraffe *loves* you, mwah! mwah!"

We run in the yard, roll the ball, listen to the scrub jay's complaints, the hush of wind, the slow regal swaying of huge trees – her eyes intense with the small everyday miracles of her hours of discovery. The air itself glinting with the million shiny leaves that seem to dance with us.

Yet I am such an habitual hour-counting adult I need to *remind* myself to slow down some, then more, then settle there – open and as joyous as this creature I'm privileged to be with.

Mwah! Mwah! I think to myself and laugh. She looks at me and laughs too. I deeply believe she gets my internal joke.

• • •

The day after Christmas at 8 p.m. I get a text from my next-door neighbor who has had a felon come to her door, talk his way into her house and when he sees that her boyfriend is there, convince him to drive him to a nearby relative's house.

She finds out the man is a COVID-positive, male-averse, female-manipulating con-man who's been stalking our street for vulnerable people and opportunities for weeks.

She tells me that he has an extensive felony criminal record in El Dorado County, including assault of women, that he is 6'3" and that if he comes to my door next that I should not engage him in conversation and call the Placerville Police.

"I don't want to alarm you...," she writes.

Her admonitions for calm are so incongruously tempered they throw me into a slow-burn panic that blooms over the hours. She has no idea how tense I've already been in fighting my own isolation and trepidation and that this is yet another last straw upon the already final straw.

I call her for more details, they are even more alarming. My other neighbor calls me repeating the same and more details which, though kind, quadruples my alarm. If I sleep for a single hour it's by accident.

For the next several weeks every time I look out any window of my home I'm checking to see if he's on my property; in my yard, approaching my door. I begin leaving my windows covered all day in addition to night. But it doesn't help. *Assaultive felon* is bleeding into COVID-19 risk into isolation into unfamiliar territory into presidential election verging on civil war. I resist leaving home for fear of finding him there when I get back. Yet I can't stand being home because I'm so frightened he might be casing my place and is intending on approaching me when I take trash out or go pick up my mail by the street.

Only on my days caring for my granddaughter do I relax, knowing I'd rip his face off of his skull if he came near her. But though the fierceness is momentarily bracing, it isn't a realistic strategy.

One day I look out the back window for the hundredth worried time and realize all I can see is the potential of the felon stalker's presence. I can no longer see the lawn, or the chairs my family and I relax on or the beautiful trees and light there.

It finally occurs to me that in my panicked myopia I have crossed some line – that I am now actually stalking myself.

So day by day, gesture by gesture, I begin to peel away my apprehension from my anticipation. It's hard work at first, seems pointless in fact, yet I keep at it. And it gains slow momentum: I see the beauty of the sun in a triangle on my granddaughter's spinning wheel on the lawn; a discarded Elmo doll hilariously sprawled gape-mouthed where she dropped him distracted by her mother's arrival. A ball left in the far corner of the garden, ready to roll and toss.

I begin to see inviting things for what they are and scary things for *if* they come, *later* or *never* but not hosted by my imagination 24/7.

I rationalize that a calm woman is a more skillfully ready woman than a terrified woman who is exhausted and apt to make mistakes. This takes time too but also builds momentum and becomes certainty. The wind-chimes ring faintly and sound beautiful instead of alarming. Delicacy and subtlety begin to return to my days. I regain some lost confidence.

It takes several weeks of almost constant effort, a new kind of vigilance — but slowly I uncover the world as it was before the stalker arrived in our neighborhood, as much at risk as any life is.

In the midst of change the drone of heart provides a warm underscore as the filigree of melody interweaves.

2020, Candle in the Dark

One locally clear day I watch rain falling from storm clouds in the far distance. From here it is a sweet and gentle curtain moving with high winds, almost waltzing with the air.

My husband's favorite saying was 'Better to light a candle than curse the darkness,' and after decades of hearing this reliably but sparingly addressed to the worst of our circumstances I am very grateful for his repetitions. In his absence I have needed to learn to light my own candles, be faithful in my own darkness.

So much of life is simply perspective, even with the no-distance-at-all of one's own circling thoughts. Now that I am further alone in a new city, new environment, new house in the midst of an isolating pandemic, I contemplate the deeper question of lighting the match, of sitting back to be reassured by the warmth of the candle light.

Perhaps it is not an action at all but just trust even in the midst of the sometimes ill-lit and humbling process of life. Humility gentle enough, like a distant curtain of rain, to surround but not to overwhelm. Humility that leaves me willingly reaching for the choices I am allowed to choose. Even in the midst of the ones for which there are no alternatives.

2020, Sparrow

you just go on with your business
soon as it stops snowing
pecking the ground
for seeds and pebbles

drinking snowmelt
from leaves
positioned in the sun

one continuous world
you, the snow, the warmth,
the leaf proffering
its cupped sustenance,

your beak busy
weaving all existence
while mindful of flight –

the universe is
so much bigger
than might seem

and in the smallest places

2020, There You Are

just as the moon
wearing the earth's curvature
clears the sequoia's highest leaves
                    seeking zenith
you are twirling your outstretched
toddler fingers in the low morning sun
looking back
to watch their dancing shadows
twirl over and over,

just like your father when young
you never tire until
you are suddenly, gently fast asleep
to dream of reaching
into the dark

on the late-afternoon lawn
I witness you watching
your long thin shadow-companion
emerge and flow inseparable
from your feet as you walk
aware for the first time
that she follows you

twenty-six degrees slanting
from your tiny-footed
gravity-tether

the simple geometry
of being alive
of the pure heart you hold
your hand out to greet
but cannot touch
again, again, laughing
and never to say good-bye

2020, Coffee

    Each and every first cup of coffee of every day I drink it is the best cup of coffee I've ever had. No cell. No sunlight for a long while yet. The sweet air filling with soft blueness is good company and we know each other well. The robins and an unusually gentle scrub jay beseech the dawn long before its molten copper body reaches between the leaves. Having become animate from the clay of earth, the birds fill the coming day with their notes of return and lovely soft pauses that loll in the cool.

    I finish my coffee among this living prayer and place the still-warm mug against my chest for its reciprocating warmth. This is the hush that holds all the love still alive from all of time without nostalgia or regret or sadness. This is the peace of communal presence as it pivots from branch to branch and into the singular endeavors of day.

2021, Fall Colors

Fall colors. Colors falling back into the earth.

I don't know what it means. It is as a beloved's hand gently slipping around mine. A subconscious, shared presence no matter the meaning: automatically I reach back, their hand instinctively curls around my reaching response.

That these yellows, greens, reds, browns and purples rise aglow from the dark soil to splay themselves suspended, then airborne, is to know inevitability, beauty, time, surrender. This happens without words, some days slowly, some all-at-once, a mutual fate made gloriously manifest without judgment or fear.

It just comes on. It paints itself everywhere individually to the leaf, is carried by the wind. It will soon be merely a memory.

For today it is only lovely to be surrounded, to breathe together.

I accept the reassurance of your hand.

I fall into rhythm with your steps.

2021, Equinox

So much purpose of thought is required to diminish thinking's overriding showiness; so much effort to access what lies beneath the sequined costume of my self-concept – to fully feel the skin, muscle, blood and bones that are enjoined in the seasons shifting.

And yet when I can, even if only for a moment, I feel naked to the air and its worldly drift, the light traveling through it, the exhalations of the plants and animals and planet traversing eternity. It is there that I know the season and its shifting as if unhurriedly and yet all-of-a-sudden, stuttering hot to cold and cold again by fate and surging restiveness.

At night the unusually full moon wakes me from its incomprehensible new position, spilling white light into the room like a thief illuminating opportunity. I open the curtain only to see that everyone equally is being cased, the goods are time and love, comfort and predictability.

Yet there is a thrill that becomes apparent as well, the thrill of change itself, new scents, new angles of light revealing unnoticed branches reaching; grey fox mates traveling the lawn at ease in the small hours; the sotto voce notes of the wind chimes profound and eloquent as grand piano chords in a darkened concert hall.

I love being transported by this thing so much bigger than I can reach my fingertips to contain, to tumble along with it, to be taken by it. I am part of the family, animate and inanimate, being carried, arms-linked, inexorably forward – created and re-created, subject and witness to the ceaseless probing of life.

2021, Dream, Buddha

He is an extraordinarily beautiful man. I am sitting across from him over a small wooden table, both of us cross-legged on pillows, and I don't feel intimidated even though my mind is tempted to be.

I can't tell if his beauty is his physicality or his whole being, his palpable presence in the room or the way he generously includes me in his own presence — easily, welcomingly, effortlessly, puts me at ease. He isn't even looking at me. Yet all of this is real in the sharing of our presences, in the texture of the air, in the light, in the sounds outside coming and going and encapsulating his and my shared quiet simply together. I know he can see me without looking up, peripherally, humanly, through our proximity. We can smell each other's bodies draped in cotton robes and yet this is simple and unremarkable.

He is eating a small bowl of rice pudding. With chopsticks. Not carefully exactly and yet so effortlessly and efficiently. He is adept and unselfconscious. Even with my own self-consciousness his calm is contagious.

I contemplate my own small bowl of rice pudding as it waits for me across the table from his. I consider the invitation of it, and I am hungry and it, too, is beautiful. And yet.

"You breathe," I observe.

"Yes," he affirms. "You are complete," he observes.

I do not affirm his observation but I take it in as a possibility.

"And you are sad," he says. "And wish not to be."

"Yes," I agree and there is no need to explain.

He shifts on his cushion, easing himself, his gentle yet alive posture. I shift as well and yet many places in my body hurt, or tug, or are tired and drooping. I sit up straighter anyway, not competitive but inspired by him. I smile and even though he is not looking at me, he then looks up and smiles also.

"You don't feel sad," I observe.

"Not at this moment," he smiles. "I appreciate your company, thank you for being here."

I think to demure but his honesty inspires. I consider the possibility that I am worthy.

"I feel better just being here," I say, not knowing the why of it.

"Yes," he says.

"I'm hungry," I say and pick up my bowl and my chopsticks and begin to eat, not slowly, but deliberately. Not carefully, but gratefully. I spill a few grains of rice, but simply keep going, as though I am alone, as though I have nothing to prove.

"Yes," he says. And we continue the rest of the meal in sweet acceptance of the simple silence. And when we are finished, we stand and bow to each other looking into each other's eyes openly, gladly and without reservation. We also part in silence. Gratefully, separately, carrying ourselves forward.

I remember the room and his presence throughout the day, its unreserved openness, its aliveness, the sounds surrounding us as I then, in turn, enter their busyness with his ease weaving its grace into my day.

2021, Time

The first among my contemporary friends has begun an obliterating slide into Alzheimer's. News that brings a silence to my days that cannot be sidestepped; an apprehension of time that I cannot calibrate — increments of disappearance.

What is outside of time? "Forever"?

An abstraction beyond my bounded hours filled with details. Is forgetting "forever?" Is it gentle? Or can one spark of remembrance inflict myriad wounds of urgency by vague implication? Irritations with no solutions? Falling dominoes.

Day-before-yesterday my neighbor needed to kill a venerable towering pine. Ever since its abysmally loud and precarious removal, an equally towering silence has called my attention to its missing height and open-armed quietude; called attention to the sound of wind brushing first its needles then thick branches then my hair and ears; has called a hush to the skyward reach of its patient nobility and the way it drew my eyes to the blue and the clouds and an unhurried beckoning expansiveness.

This has intertwined with my friend whose shared memories with me will cease by stealth. This brings existential questions to all of our friends about our shared history, about the shared wisdom still living in our lives. About shared afternoons of picnics and slightly inebriated candle-lit paper-plate celebratory meals. The musicality and authority of an admired strong friend entering obliteration.

And yet while playing in the yard with my granddaughter, accompanied only by the sure voices of scrub jays, flickers and robins and the single words this sweet child speaks and the grandma encouragements I fill her ears with, I hear the no-longer-tree's silence and my friend's soon silence and I am deeply saddened and then unaccountably at peace.

This small child and I are surrounded by a texture so subtle it begs our astonished wonderment, stops our play. It is an entity released from its container and we are immersed in its substanceless flood.

My granddaughter looks up at the wind's effects and the light and I say, yes, isn't it beautiful and her eyes don't waver or answer but rather they look more intently at what she is seeing so that I look again to see what she is seeing. It is the leaves shaking off the light as it spills from and refills their dancing surfaces. She just laughs, as if in answer to something that has spoken to us.

And yet no one has spoken.

Even after my neighbor's magnificent tree is down, even after its base is ground to level to make way for a patio, this towering being has left us at peace. The highest reach has fallen to the lowest point and seeped in to the deepest roots where the disturbing music of that flight has become a most tender open question.

That needs no answer.

My granddaughter and I return to playing and I know she will let this hour lie ambient within herself as she gathers language and numbers and preference and presence in the world. That they will lie rooted to this spring day, to this moment in time, beneath her memories. I'll know it's there in her and watch with delight as the simple texture of these hours echo her growing complexity of joys and loves.

Knowing that "forever" and memory are only concepts after all and peace is what lies under the passing of each thought just as the notes of music flow through the open arms of silence.

2021, Adaptation

The long-run cat
is nearly nineteen —
I don't know if she loves me but

I feed her,
so perhaps the gestures
I take for affection
are just another form
of hunting.

She finds me
to share body-warmth
on most cold nights
but in summer
when it sears
she sleeps atop the clean
cool laundry
so I need to wash it again.

She interrupts my sleep
as my husband used to do
rustling in the dark to attend
to various comforts
and in this way

she keeps me human.

She has a habit to rest
in a spill of sunlight
wherever it moves
the way a carried child instinctively
rests one hand
upon her parent's cheek.

I don't know if she loves me,
we simply keep each other true.

2021, Napping in the Storm

The sound falls onto the roof and into my consciousness first as a delicate thing, unaware of itself, entering by only a single sense from the sky and yet so completely.

The first drops are tentative, alluring, attention-getting: this. this, this, that. this, that, this. this this, this, this. I look over at my napping granddaughter as the sound gathers, grows, escalates to a constant.

The sound of it is delicious and collaborative and I feel my joy reach to the ceiling with my mind's hand to touch this alive thing that in turn is reaching down to me. I sense the joy all around me as everything needs this essential moisture.

All around the house the shadowy trees are beginning to drink and reach their roots deeper into the thirst-slackening earth. Shadow beneath shadow; shadow rising into the house and with it I turn more warm lights on inside, accentuating the movement *in* that we are all participating in in our different ways.

My granddaughter on her little nap couch is away inside herself as well, dreaming something that makes her fingers curl and dance. The cat suspects it is safe to come out and tentatively nears to inspect the sleeping child, reassuring herself it is safe to roam.

Now the rain is building in intensity and sounds like lightly sizzling food cooking. But soon is a basso overwhelm. With its strength I am more aware than ever of all of the people out there under freeway overpasses or even on creek sides under tarps becoming more alarmed as the storm's vehemence grows and sustains for hour upon hour and the flowing water rises all around.

I wish we could all help each other in a concerted way. And yet we all continue separate as our fates and our choices enclose us, drop by drop, flow by flow. It is musical chairs and suddenly we are all on the last chair yet somehow separately. Wishing the others were within reach.

I can only be grateful for the beauty and safety I have right now and for it I am deeply grateful. I send my prayers out.

Even as I gently stroke my granddaughter's back to try and wake her from the long nap the rain concert keeps her in, she is away, away — playing in her future, the puzzle pieces fitting or not fitting, but she keeps trying and brilliantly, finally, finds some logic only her own imagination offers. She smiles in her sleep.

Like the rain, I only see one aspect of her sleep-gentled face and yet I am grateful to be here with her to blindly witness the path only she can actually see, reaching towards it.

2021, Social Medium

I wake in a remnant dream that diffuses into dawn
light infusing the windows and air, curtains made of
bedsheets, all interweaving

you are the coffee man; the man who comes home
every night; the man who can sleep no matter what.
yet for twenty-six years when I sigh, you wake to re-
assure me

fourteen years ago one night you cannot sleep you
don't know why; three years of diagnoses then we
find out. sixteen months of dying then we part

dawn is a sigh-like touch and I sense we are together
perhaps never separate. the darkness seeps back into
the earth like rain accepted.

your toddler granddaughter in her highchair pauses
and regards me with old-soul eyes. generational
glance? from long before you died?

we share the room despite physics. she naps through
anything, she mimics my sigh. I see that you see me
through the telescope of her being

bare feet on tiles making coffee, I feel myself a limit-less sphere both centered in and unbounded by my individual life. odd comfort.

showering during rain midmorning, water sound and rain sound in concentric built cubes. open window to the clean air wash of leaves laughing

no controlling who enters or exits our lives. can only feel our hearts wishing one gone, wishing another still here. careful path through the hours

the epigenetic psychs say firstborn has the parents' trauma, the second born, their grandparents'. linked hands, a dance around the bonfire

where I was born – waves, sand, sinking footprints. now, forest roots linked by sentient fungi, ground giving and taking, weave and yield.

released felon stalks; covid kills; and yet – gilded hours with your toddler innocence, your mom, your dad. sacred ballast, our humanity.

2021, Contrail

into the thin blue caul of breath
surrounding our mother planet
a line both writes
and erases itself silently
high above our gazes
there for anyone to read,
this reality is also our mother

to look up, to break stride
to pause quietly
and recognize
this mechanistic human cursive
beyond language,
this is also our mother.

even my toddler granddaughter
as we sit together
on the back lawn playing
watches the soft white script at zenith
mesmerized
to see it become and unbecome itself
on the empty borderless page of sky
bubble-wand forgotten in my hand
bubbles riding the wind uncaught

both of us quieted,
accepting the high-sky poem
that whispers
only in the native language of our hearts

2021, Earth's Felt Mirror

Lingering fire season, slept on the living room couch so I could hear an evacuation knock in the middle of the night. Dreamed continuously — crowded shifting delighted allegiances handing off each to each as in a folk dance. Woke with these companions retreating and my whole chest tensed as if bending forward to chase them.

Yet my waking mind had already begun reluctantly pacing down knowing that Dream had outdistanced me. Recognized the longing and reaching that are the signs of the lost linkage, the wistful countenance of shifted consciousness. My muscles still filled with dream. My heart still holding its wisdom without detail: an intimately familiar archetype without face as though someone is moving away from me in the house switching off the lights as they go and finally now, from the farthest room, only a pale diaphanous rectangle of light through the doorway lingers.

Who visited me? I need them! And yet I can still feel them, in my lungs as a scent/flavor; in my muscles as a carried, mute knowing; in my volition as a craving for continuity with these timeless collaborators. But the realities of my daily efforts feel like so many ellipses between illuminations that dilute themselves in the living.

Perhaps the continuity is not in the schedule and its accomplishments but in my heart, in its sense of me in the world and in my life, not changing with moods or textures or contacts with people, but only with a steady sense of continuance. I feel the truth of this viscerally as though I have incorporated the dream in my waking world without recalling its story. A subtle texture of light; a certain knowing; a knowing with certainty.

Can I let go of the reaching toward it? Can I know it without defining the type of knowledge? This feels like the deepest kind of knowing.

true to form, this face
I've never directly seen — in the
cool fall air, earth's felt mirror

2022, We Meet Again

You walk toward me
through bright sunlight,
into shadow
and into sunlight again –
lit, obscured, lit.

You are tall
and beautiful and
I see that
you are at ease
with yourself
by the rhythm
of your long, unhurried gait.

For a moment it seems
you are looking at me
but I am wrong, embarrassed,
and look away and back.
You advance
toward me.

It is only when
I no longer mistake
our knowing one another

that I see you are
pleasurably intent:

with what
I cannot say;
with whom
I cannot know.

2022, New Territory

the murmuring passenger jet high above
the crisp closer signature of a biplane
suggest freedom
as they wander the sky,

the world enters through sound
airy road signs that call to home

all day
all night

and inside
the wood creaks its commentary
the cat crunches her kibble
my granddaughter argues
swift syllables from her dream, kicking
then settles as peace personified

this is what the blue dawn light seeps into
on this day at this moment
simply elegant –

the same old track,
brand new territory

Mockingbird

This first hot night of summer
you sing your song into the darkness
weaving entrancement
through our restless sleep
your notes so insistent so tender
they fly through the starlight
right into our dreams

and each of us awakens separately
and all of us together recognize
your ancestral song
and your ventriloquist's sleight-of-voice
of our Sunday motorcycles revving
of our alarm systems cycling
of our bursts of laughter
over fences

you write a scroll upon the infinite
your body light as air

hunching and rising
on your drought-dusty lemon leaf
that reflects your song back to you
as if your mate is already answering

and your voice strengthens
through the open windows
where we've given up on sleep
and you enter our waking dreams
with love and the relief of dawn,

your species our species, the tumbling of light
through the hours each note
so full of the urge for continuance
we ache toward you
not exactly knowing why
your tireless call insists
we rise to the mutual hour
of our shared possibility.

ABOUT THE AUTHOR

Jemi Reis McDonald is a California native, lifelong writer, twenty-two year Soto Zen Buddhist practitioner, decades-long wife, mother, new grandmother and enduring friend. And despite many human errors along the way, she counts her continuing endeavor to purify her own heart and her collaboration with unending change as her hardest, wisest and most valuable individual accomplishments.

Made in the USA
Middletown, DE
07 November 2022

14220004R00068